How Many Peas in a Pod?

Margaret Allum and Judy Watson

BACK**PACK**BOOKS

NEW YORK

How many cows in a cornfield?

How many pigs in a pen?

How many bears in a bed?

How many pumpkins in a patch?

How many cats in a clothes basket?

How many peas in a pod?

How many toucans in a tree?

How many socks in a suitcase?

How many bubbles in a bathtub?

How many lizards on a log?

How many jellybeans in a jar?

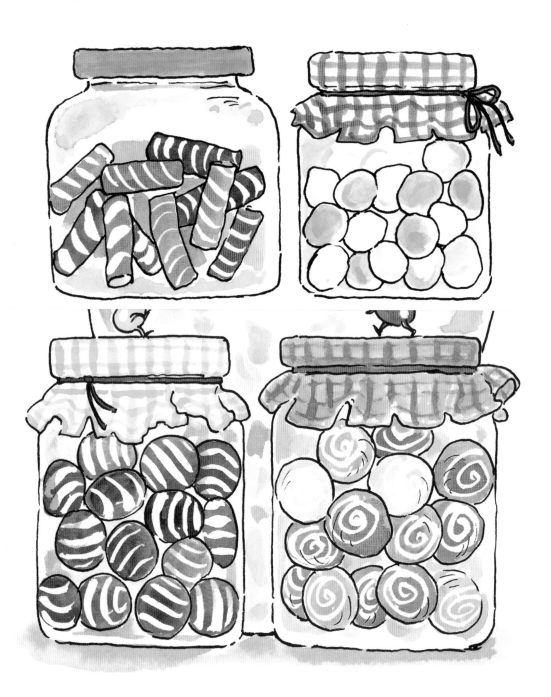

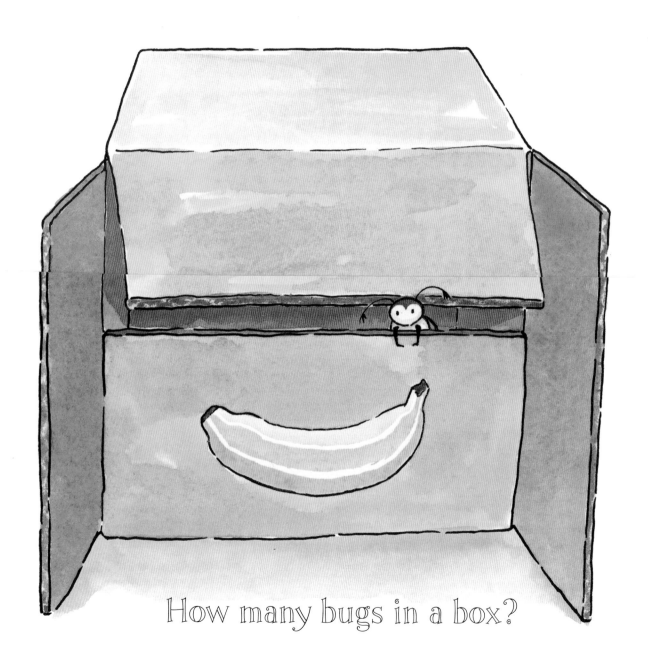

How many bugs in a box?

How many flowers in a field?

For Arthur's grandparents - JW